# Peppa Pig™

# Nature Trail

Mummy and Daddy Pig ask Peppa if she can
see anything interesting in the forest.
"I don't see anything but boring trees," says Peppa.
Then, she looks really hard and
finds some footprints on the ground.

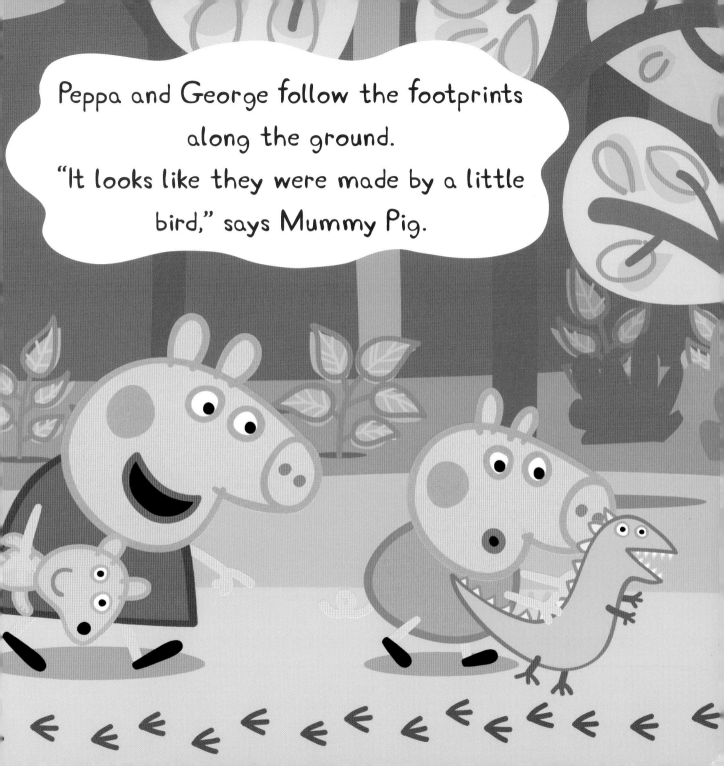

Soon, they come to the
end of the footprints.
"The bird has flown up into
that tree," smiles Daddy Pig.

George finds some more footprints. They
are very little. Daddy Pig says they belong
to ants collecting leaves to eat.

"My map is wrong," begins Daddy Pig. "We'll have to follow our own footprints back to the car."

"Ducks love picnics," says Peppa. "Mrs Duck, can you help us find our picnic please?"

And so do the ants! Munch! Munch! "Everybody loves picnics!" cries Peppa.